ODYSSEY

THE ADVENTURE OF LEARNING

A JOURNAL

D1273902

This book belongs to:

Year:

Writing is how we think our way into a subject
and make it our own.
Writing enables us to find out what we know
—and what we don't know.

—William Zinsser, *Writing to Learn*

Contents

©2021 Denise Gaskins, denisegaskins.com. All rights reserved. Tabletop Academy Press.

CREDITS: Cover image by grandfailure, Depositphotos.

Learning is a Lifelong Journey

The adventure of learning doesn't belong only in school. It happens whenever a curious mind meets a new idea.

And when we write about what we're learning, we build deeper layers of understanding. The process of wrestling our ideas into words forces us to pin down nebulous thoughts and decide what we really believe. It can even help us develop a richer mathematical mindset.

You can use this journal for homework, or for recreational math investigations, or as a planner. It provides a great place to keep track of your thoughts, dreams, and discoveries. Record memories, keep track of tasks, solve challenge problems, design your own puzzles. Brainstorm for projects, jot down ideas, work out problems, or doodle geometric designs.

Or make it a reading journal. Write down each book you read, with its author and year of publication. Tell whether you liked the book or not, and why. Is it worth re-reading someday?

How to Freewrite

Freewriting sparks creative thought by removing any need to worry about punctuation or grammar rules. Write fast and raw—whatever comes into your mind.

Your only goal is to put words down on the paper. And then keep writing until you reach the end of the page.

Don't overthink it, just write.

Respond to the Quotes

When you find a quote or saying that you particularly like, respond to it from your own perspective. If you like, try one of the essay question ideas below.

Short-Response Prompts

- What did the author mean? Put the thought in your own words.
- Do you agree or disagree? Explain.
- Is it a general principle, or only for specific situations? Describe a time when the quote might apply, or when it might not.
- Tell a time in your life when you lived up to the quotation—or when you wish you had.
- How does the quote relate to math, science, history, or another subject?

Research Prompts

- Look up the author's name online. Who are/were they? Why do people care what they said?
- What have others said about the same topic? Search out a variety of quotes related to this one. How are they similar? How are they different?
- Does thinking about the quotation make you want to change anything, in yourself or in the world? How could you put that idea into action?

Join the Math Rebellion

Math rebels write any true answer *except* what the textbook expects.

For example, if the textbook answer is 57, a rebel might write:

$100 - 43$

or $2 \times 5^2 + 7$

or $^{120}/_2 + (-3)$

or

"The total number of mushrooms in the basket, if three hobbits each picked nineteen 'shrooms (not counting the ones they ate)."

Math rebels can make the answer as crazy as they like. Have fun!

Understand the Math

When you get a math worksheet or homework page, don't start working straight away. First, examine the page to see if the problems look familiar. Do you know what the teacher or textbook wants you to do?

Math rebels always care about the truth. So first, learn what the problem means and how to figure it out. After you know how to solve the problem, then you can start working on your creative answer.

Choose Your Battleground

Fighting for intellectual freedom takes energy, so decide how rebellious you want to be. Are you going to mess with just a few of the problems? Or turn the whole page into a protest statement?

Live by the Two Rules

You are allowed to write anything that is true. You are not allowed to write anything that is not true.

Those are the important rules of mathematics. Anything else is just advice—follow it only when it helps you on your current problem.

Creative Calculation Ideas

Can you write an answer that includes:

- More than two numbers?
- A number ending in 3 or 7? (Because those often seem randomish.)
- A number greater than 100? Greater than 1,000?
- A number in the 9 times table?
- Money? Or some kind of measurement?
- A prime number? A square number?
- A fraction or decimal? A fraction or decimal greater than one?
- A negative integer?
- A geometric diagram?
- A square or cube root?
- A complex fraction? That is, a fraction that contains another fraction in its numerator, denominator, or both.

Or Make a Commonplace Book

Leonardo da Vinci described his notebook as "A collection without order, drawn from many papers, which I have copied here, hoping to arrange them later each in its place, according to the subjects of which they treat."

Throughout history, famous people and just-plain-ordinary folk have kept notes of the things they find interesting—witty sayings, recipes, project ideas, sketches, quotations like those in this book—collecting them all one common place for easy reference.

To make this journal your commonplace book, keep it handy throughout the day. Whether you are reading a library book or browsing online, make a note of anything that stands out. Copy down short phrases or longer passages, poems, snappy comebacks, jokes, song lyrics, anecdotes or other tidbits.

Writing things down by hand helps them stick in your memory, even if you never go back and read your notes. But the greatest value of a commonplace book comes when you page back though it. You will find serendipitous connections between ideas or thoughts that didn't seem related to each other. Such surprises can become inspiration for your own creativity or lead you to new discoveries.

Over time, the journal entries become a record of your personal odyssey of adventurous learning.

The cure for boredom is curiosity. There is no cure for curiosity.

—DOROTHY PARKER

The only real mistake is the one from which we learn nothing.

—John Powell

Education is the key to unlock the golden door of freedom.

—George Washington Carver

Inspiration usually comes during work, rather than before it.

—Madeleine L'Engle

I like to listen. I have learned a great deal from listening carefully. Most people never listen.

—Ernest Hemingway

That is what learning is. You suddenly understand something you've understood all your life, but in a new way.

—Doris Lessing

I'm a great believer in luck, and I find the harder I work the more I have of it.

—Thomas Jefferson

If you think you can do a thing or think you can't do a thing, you're right.

—Henry Ford

The excitement of learning separates youth from old age. As long as you're learning, you're not old.

—Rosalyn S. Yallow

It is what we think we know already that often prevents us from learning.

—Claude Bernard

An education isn't how much you have committed to memory, or even how much you know. It's being able to differentiate between what you know and what you don't.

—Anatole France

The difference between school and life? In school, you're taught a lesson and then given a test. In life, you're given a test that teaches you a lesson.

—Tom Bodett

Man's mind stretched to a new idea never goes back to its original dimensions.

—Oliver Wendell Holmes, Jr.

Opportunity is missed by most people because it is dressed in overalls and looks like work.

—Thomas Edison

You don't educate people by telling them useful things, you educate them by telling them interesting things.

—John Conway

Learning is not attained by chance, it must be sought for with ardor and attended to with diligence.

—Abigail Adams

A great memory does not make a mind, any more than a dictionary is a piece of literature.

—John Henry Newman

But it's not just learning things that's important. It's learning what to do with what you learn and learning why you learn things at all that matters.

—Norton Juster

Nothing in life is to be feared, it is only to be understood. Now is the time to understand more, so that we may fear less.

—Marie Curie

Knowing others is intelligence; knowing yourself is true wisdom.
Mastering others is strength, mastering yourself is true power.

—Lao-Tzu

Learning without thought is labor lost; thought without learning is perilous.

—Confucius

The most exciting phrase to hear in science, the one that heralds new discoveries, is not “Eureka!” (I found it!) but “That’s funny…”

—Isaac Asimov

The real voyage of discovery consists not in seeking new lands, but in seeing with new eyes.

—Marcel Proust

I don't love studying. I hate studying. I like learning. Learning is beautiful.

—Natalie Portman

Before you act, listen. Before you react, think. Before you spend, earn. Before you criticize, wait. Before you pray, forgive. Before you quit, try.

—Ernest Hemingway

When you do the common things in life in an uncommon way, you will command the attention of the world.

—George Washington Carver

Winning doesn't always mean being first. Winning means you're doing better than you've done before.

—Bonnie Blair

Education is the ability to listen to almost anything without losing your temper or your self-confidence.

— Robert Frost

Everybody, sooner or later, sits down to a banquet of consequences.

—Robert Louis Stevenson

It *always* seems impossible until it is done.

—Nelson Mandela

Even if you are on the right track, you will get run over if you just sit there.

—Will Rogers

To do the useful thing, to say the courageous thing, to contemplate the beautiful thing: that is enough for one man's life.

—T. S. Eliot

Yesterday is history. Tomorrow is a mystery. Today is a gift. That's why we call it 'The Present'.

—Eleanor Roosevelt

The time is *always* right to do *what* is right.

—Martin Luther King, Jr.

When I get a little money I buy books; and if any is left I buy food and clothes.

—Erasmus

The secret to learning is so simple: forget about it. Think only about whatever you love. Follow it, do it, dream it.

—Grace Llewellyn

The length of your education is less important than its breadth, and the length of your life is less important than its depth.

—Marilyn vos Savant

It’s not what happens to you, but how you react to it that matters.

—Epictetus

The man who does not read good books has no advantage over the man who can't read them.

—Mark Twain

To doubt everything, or, to believe everything, are two equally convenient solutions; both dispense with the necessity of reflection.

—Henri Poincare

A little learning is a dangerous thing; drink of it deeply, or taste it not, for shallow thoughts intoxicate the brain, and drinking deeply sobers us again.

—Alexander Pope

One's work may be finished someday, but one's education never.

—Alexandre Dumas

An investment in knowledge always pays the best interest.

—Benjamin Franklin

We are what we repeatedly do. Excellence then is not an act, but a habit.

—Aristotle

We must learn to live together as brothers or perish together as fools.

—Martin Luther King, Jr.

The clearer the teacher makes it, the worse it is for you. You must work things out for yourself and make the ideas your own.

—William F. Osgood

We learn more by looking for the answer to a question and not finding it than we do from learning the answer itself.

—Lloyd Alexander

Remember that joy and passion lead to more learning than duty ever did.

—Sue VanHattum

Human beings, who are almost unique in having the ability to learn from the experience of others, are also remarkable for their apparent disinclination to do so.

—Douglas Adams

That which is hateful to you, do not do to your fellow. That is the whole Torah; the rest is the explanation; go and learn.

—Hillel the Elder

The beautiful thing about learning is nobody can take it away from you.

—B. B. King

Learning proceeds until death and only then does it stop ... Its purpose cannot be given up for even a moment. To pursue it is to be human, to give it up to be a beast.

—Xun Zi